The Foolish Fox

Written by Alison Hawes

Illustrated by Matte Stephens

OXFORD
UNIVERSITY PRESS

Fox

Sheep

Fox had a farm but he
did not like farming.

So he said to some sheep, "Farm my land for me, and you can keep some of the food."

The sheep said, "Can we keep the *top* part of the food or the *bottom* part?" "The top part," said Fox.

5

So the sheep put corn seeds in the soil.

When the corn was high,
the sheep cut it down.

Then they took the corn
roots to Fox.

"This is not food!" said Fox.
Fox was cross. It had been a trick!

9

So the sheep put turnip
seeds in the soil.

When the turnips were big,
the sheep dug them up.

They took the turnip tops to Fox.

"This is not food!" said Fox.
Fox was cross. It had been a trick!

So now, Fox farms his land himself!

OXFORD
UNIVERSITY PRESS

Great Clarendon Street, Oxford, OX2 6DP, United Kingdom

Oxford University Press is a department of the University
of Oxford. It furthers the University's objective of excellence
in research, scholarship, and education by publishing
worldwide. Oxford is a registered trade mark of Oxford University Press
in the UK and in certain other countries

Text © Oxford University Press 2011
Illustrations © Matte Stephens 2011

The moral rights of the author have been asserted

First published 2011

This edition published 2019

British Library Cataloguing in Publication Data
Data available

ISBN: 978-0-19-277221-3

10 9 8 7 6 5 4 3 2 1

Paper used in the production of this book is a natural, recyclable
product made from wood grown in sustainable forests. The
manufacturing process conforms to the environmental
regulations of the country of origin.

Printed in China

Acknowledgements

Series Advisor: Nikki Gamble